ball
sports

robert sandelson

Crestwood House
New York

Maxwell Macmillan International
New York   Oxford   Singapore   Sydney

OLYMPIC SPORTS

OLYMPIC SPORTS

TRACK ATHLETICS
FIELD ATHLETICS
SWIMMING AND DIVING
GYMNASTICS
ICE SPORTS
SKIING
BALL SPORTS
COMBAT SPORTS

Designer: Joyce Chester
Editor: Deborah Elliott

Cover: Teresa Weatherspoon of the United States looks for a possible scoring opportunity in the final of the women's basketball competition in Seoul in 1988. The United States defeated the Yugoslavians 77 – 70 to win the gold medal.

CRESTWOOD HOUSE
Macmillan Publishing Company
866 Third Avenue
New York, NY 10022

Macmillan Publishing Company is part of the Maxwell Communication Group of Companies

First published in Great Britain in 1991
by Wayland (Publishers) Ltd
61 Western Road, Hove, East Sussex BN3 1JD

Printed in Italy by G. Canale & C.S.p.A.
1 2 3 4 5 6 7 8 9 10

ACKNOWLEDGMENTS

The Publisher would like to thank the following agencies and photographers for allowing their pictures to be reproduced in this book: All Sport *cover*, 5, 16 (David Cannon), 17 (Billy Strickland), 23 (Simon Bruty), 24 (Pascal Rondeau), 25 (Pascal Rondeau), 26 (Pascal Rondeau), 34 (both Joe Patronite), 36 (Joe Patronite), 42 (Mike Powell), 43 (Mike Powell), 44 (bottom, Bruce Hazelton) (top, Bob Martin), 45 (both, Bruce Hazelton); Associated Sports Photography 19; BBC Hulton Picture Library 13, 29, 30; Colorsport 9, 10, 11, 15, 22, 27 (S. Fraser), 28, 35, 36 (bottom); Popperfoto 14, 18; Topham Picture Library 7, 8, 20, 21, 31, 33, 36 (bottom), 38, 39, 40.

Library of Congress Cataloging-in-Publication Data

Sandelson, Robert.
   Ball Sports / by Robert Sandelson.
      p.   cm. — (Olympic sports)
   Reprint. First published: Hove, East Sussex:
Wayland Publishers. 1991.
      Includes bibliographical references and index.
      Summary: Provides a history of the inclusion in
the Olympic program of six ball sports: tennis,
soccer, hockey, handball, basketball and volleyball.
   ISBN 0-89686-664-5
      1. Ball games — Juvenile literature.
      2. Olympics — Juvenile literature.
      |1. Ball games. 2. Olympics.| I. Title.
GV861.S26   1991
796.3 — dc20   91-21804
                                                      CIP
                                                       AC

CONTENTS

BALL SPORTS

There are currently six ball sports in the Olympic program — tennis, soccer, field hockey, handball, basketball, and volleyball. At Seoul in 1988 two others were added as ''demonstration'' events, which means that they are tried out for possible inclusion — these were baseball and table tennis. *Pelota,* a game similar to jai alai, was included in the schedule for the 1992 Games.

The argument for the inclusion of table tennis came mainly from the Olympic hosts in 1988, the South Koreans. They had beaten the Chinese in the Asian Games of 1986 and felt confident of medals on their home ground. As it turned out they were right. And although there was a losing South Korean in the final of the men's singles, he lost to another one of his countrymen. The baseball competition was won by the American team; the Japanese finished in second place. The American victory was not unexpected considering it is the country's national game. Whether either or both of these sports take root in the Olympic movement is yet to be seen. From the history of the Olympics we find that ball sports have a remarkable ability to come and go.

Discontinued events

The two games that had the biggest following before their eventual demise were rugby and polo. The reason for rugby's original instatement as an Olympic sport was the enthusiasm of the Olympic movement's founder, Baron Pierre de Coubertin. The rugby-football match held in Paris in 1900 between recent adversaries in the Franco-Prussian war, France and Germany, was a great success. Especially since France ultimately took the gold, with the favorites, Britain, coming in third.

Eight years later in London the only two entrants were Australia and Britain. The Australians won convincingly 32 − 3. The next, and what then turned out to be the last, two tournaments in 1920 and 1924 were both won by the United States. Outsiders in the rugby world, the American team called on the considerable talents of their top sprinters. In 1920, the American team had the 100-m specialist and gold and silver sprint medal winner Morris Kirksey, as well as the experienced Daniel Caroll. He had played for the winning Australian team twelve years earlier. The team beat France 8 − 0. Four years later, the French crowd of 30,000 was shocked to see its home team beaten by the Americans. The American team was accused of unfair play, and rugby disappeared completely from the Olympic Games.

Polo had some success. A crowd of 45,000 watched the Argentinians beat the British in Berlin in 1936, for their

second successive win. Polo did not, however, survive World War II. Because of the expense involved in staging the event, it has never returned to the Olympic program.

Games such as golf, cricket, roque, rackets, and croquet all made appearances in early Olympic Games only to disappear in quick succession. We are now left with a small core of exciting ball sports that add enor-

▲ Table tennis was included in the 1988 Games in Seoul as a demonstration event. The winner of the women's competition was Jing Chen of China.

mously to the pleasure of the Olympic Games. Since worldwide participation in these is far greater than for some other Olympic events, their place in the Olympic movement ensures the world's continuing fascination with the Games.

TENNIS

O f all the sports that have been a part of the Olympic Games, it is tennis that has the most colorful past. Its history somehow reflects the way the world has thought about the Olympic movement altogether.

Tennis was one of only nine sports at the modern Olympics in 1896 in Athens. In the years that followed, the tennis tournament was played by the best athletes in the game. The exception to this was the disastrous Games in 1912 in Stockholm. The organizers found that because it clashed with the professional tennis championships at Wimbledon, the standard of Olympic competition by amateurs dropped considerably. The problem was that tennis stars were being increasingly well paid and Wimbledon had a longer history and more prestige than the modern Olympics. The players found themselves in an awkward position — the pressures of amateurism could hardly be balanced against their professional earnings. This was the issue over which the International Tennis Federation (ITF) and the International Olympic Committee (IOC) disagreed. The ITF wanted the right to define who was and who was not an amateur player. This disagreement led to tennis being dropped from the Games for sixty-four years.

In the 1960s tennis began to be an issue again as Philippe Chartier campaigned for its reinclusion. He championed the argument that no matter how professional the tennis circuit was, the players would compete in the Olympics purely for the honor, in true Olympic fashion. Many other sportsmen and women were using the Olympics to secure their reputations and thus their careers. Any professional tennis player would have nothing to gain from participation except an unselfish celebration of Olympic sports. Chartier argued that the supreme professional would participate as the ideal amateur. The other strong argument for its reinclusion was that it would encourage the development of the sport, especially in those developing countries where government aid for sports was restricted to events that were part of the Olympic Games. In response to these arguments, tennis was granted ''demonstration'' status in the 1968 and 1984 Games. In 1968 two of the world's best players, Manuel Santana and Helga Niessen, won the men's and women's singles competitions respectively. However, it was another twenty years before tennis really began to reenter the Olympic Games.

To start at the beginning, it was in 1896 that men's singles and doubles competitions were first held. The winner, indeed double winner, was an Irishman, John Pius Boland. Legend

Winner of the tennis ''demonstration'' men's event in 1968, Manuel Santana.

surrounds his entry into the tournament. One story has it that he was told about the Olympics by a Greek friend while he was studying at Oxford University in England. Since he wanted to participate, he went on the off-chance that he might be able to compete. He entered the singles and won. Then, when one of two German players fell ill he teamed up with the other, Fritz Traun, and they beat a Greek team by two sets to none. This Irish/German collaboration was the perfect example of the Olympic spirit — harmony among nations rather than strife. It is, however, unusual for such collaborations to occur, though this does not mean that athletes do not compete in good spirit. On this occasion the dream of non-nationalistic Olympism was spoiled when the organizers raised the British flag at the medal ceremony. Boland complained, demanding to see the Irish flag instead.

The other, more fanciful, story about John Boland is that he was coincidentally on vacation in Greece and, wanting a game of tennis but unable to find a partner or court available, he entered the Olympics. Take your choice!

Four years later, women's tennis was admitted to the 1900 Paris Olympics, twenty-eight years before the first women's track and field events were held. The first winner of the tennis event was therefore the first-ever woman Olympic gold medalist. This honor went to Britain's Charlotte Cooper. She had already won Wimbledon three times, so her victory hardly came as a shock. She went on to win the Wimbledon title five times in all, and was one of a string of top women players who dominated Wimbledon and won the Olympic title as well.

The dominant figure after Charlotte Cooper left the scene, and after World War I, was Suzanne Lenglen of France. She won two gold medals in the 1920 Games in Antwerp, which was the first to include all five tennis events — two singles and three doubles. She won the singles and mixed doubles, and only a weak

▼ Four of the main challengers for the 1920 women's Olympic title pose for the photographers. The eventual winner, Suzanne Lenglen of France (left), also won the mixed doubles.

▲ Tennis was revived as an Olympic sport as a demonstration event in Los Angeles in 1984. The winner of the women's competition, Steffi Graf of Germany, also won the event in 1988.

partner cost her the women's doubles title. Lenglen was followed by Helen Wills in 1924 in Paris, who continued the dominating form. Helen Wills, later Helen Wills Moody, from California, was known as "Little Miss Poker Face" because her fierce concentration on court was obvious from her facial expression. Her baseline game was deadly accurate, and for fifteen years she was at the top of the tennis world. But as tennis grew in importance at the Olympics, the problems of its inclusion also grew. Helen Wills Moody turned out to be the last Olympic champion for sixty-four years.

In Los Angeles in 1984, tennis was revived as a demonstration sport for players aged twenty-one and under.

The first Olympic champion since the great Helen Wills was Steffi Graf of Germany, a great talent and worthy successor to the title. Such was the success of the Los Angeles experiment that it was decided to include the event in Seoul in 1988 without age restrictions and with medals. These Games came at a fairy-tale time for Steffi Graf. She had just won the Grand Slam of major titles with victories in the French, U.S., and Australian Open championships, as well as Wimbledon. Then two weeks later she was battling it out with

arch rival Gabriela Sabatini of Argentina for the Olympic gold. In Sabatini's case, she was determined to win her country's first gold medal since 1952. As it was she had to settle for second, but even this silver medal was Argentina's first in sixteen years.

In the men's competition there were some early upsets as the seeded Henri Leconte of France was beaten by little-known Korean Kim Su, much to the delight of the home crowd. Leconte was one of the top players on the world circuit. In the final between Miloslav Mecir of Czechoslovakia and Tim Mayotte of the United States, the Czech was eager to do well so that his own country would increase investment in the sport. He started badly, losing the first set, but he broke Mayotte's serve in the first game of the second set. By countering Mayotte's attacking play at the net, he went on to win the match. Mecir had had a much harder time in the semifinal where he had been taken to five sets by Sweden's Stefan Edberg, the winner in Los Angeles. The quality of play and the sportsmanship displayed by all the players were well appreciated. Players competing for nothing but the honor were indeed a credit to the Olympic movement.

▲ Argentinian Gabriela Sabatini smashes a backhand shot across the net in the final of the women's singles competition in Seoul. Sabatini lost to Steffi Graf. Her silver medal was Argentina's first Olympic medal in sixteen years.

▶ The talented Miloslav Mecir of Czechoslovakia. Mecir's combination of delicate touches, subtlety, and sheer power was enough to give him victory in the 1988 men's Olympic final.

SOCCER

Soccer was the first team game to be included in the Olympic Games. A tournament was held in Athens in 1906; the Greek team from Smyrna was beaten in the final by a Danish team. The first Olympic soccer tournament was held in London in 1908, after the founding of the Federation of International Football Associations (FIFA) in 1904. The French influence was obviously very great. Somehow they were allowed to enter two teams in 1908. It did them no good; both were badly beaten by Denmark. In the second match, Sophus Neilsen of Denmark scored ten goals, setting up his final total of 13 Olympic points. Only Antal Dunai of Hungary has ever equaled this total.

The 1908 soccer final was between Britain and Denmark. Among the players on the British team was one member of the Football League's last amateur forward line, Hubert "Harry" Stapley, a schoolteacher. Harry played in Britain for West Ham and Glossop, where his fellow strikers were all amateurs. He was a skillful center-forward, using his speed and balance to get him into the right positions from where he could knock the ball into the goal. But the Danes, even with their prolific scorer Neilsen, could not penetrate the British defense. Two quick goals while the Danes were still finding their feet put the seal on the match. Four years later in Stockholm, the same teams faced each other again. This time the Danes lost one of their best players to injury as they were battling back into the game at 2—1 down. They could do nothing as the British team capitalized on their disarray with two quick goals.

The history of Olympic soccer is similar in some respects to that of tennis, except that soccer has survived its controversies. The tennis authorities, however, ensured their sport's exclusion when the arguments turned to rage. The reason for the controversy in soccer, as with tennis, was the definition of amateur status and the growing importance of the World Cup, a professional soccer competition. The reason the Olympic soccer tournament has been sustained is its ability to draw crowds and attract sponsorship. The scale of interest has always been taken into consideration by organizing committees. In 1984 in Los Angeles, soccer was the best attended Olympic event, yet the United States does not have a professional soccer league.

In 1924 in Paris, the final between Switzerland and Uruguay was watched by 60,000 people. The emergence of the Uruguayans added a new spark to the game. The flamboyant footwork and team play of the South Americans proved to be a great crowd-pleaser. Among their

▲ The 1936 soccer final was between Austria and Italy. Here, the Austrian goalkeeper saves a goal. However, he could not prevent the Italians from emerging as two-goal victors.

ranks was Pedro Petrone. At just eighteen years old he was the youngest-ever team gold medalist. He was a brilliant player who was partly responsible for the popularity of soccer at the Olympics. Four years later he went back with half of the previous Uruguayan team to the Games in Amsterdam. Here another South American team, Argentina, made their presence felt. The final went to two overtimes before the Uruguayans finally won. In 1930 this team went to the first World Cup and won. From this point on the World Cup had far greater prestige than the Olympic Soccer tournament. In 1936 the Italians were the last team to hold both titles at once.

After World War II, as professionals began to be systematically excluded from the Olympics, the East Europeans with their questionable amateur status dominated the game for thirty years. The Olympic game bore little relation to the world game. Except for Hungary's win in Helsinki in 1952, which was followed by their

▲ The Hungarian soccer team dominated the Olympic tournament in Helsinki in 1952. The players went on to score a memorable 6–3 victory over England the following year.

famous defeat of England sixteen months later, the two tournaments hardly reflected each other. In the following years Hungary won twice more, and the Soviet Union, Poland, and Czechoslovakia also won golds.

In 1984, because of the East European boycott of the Olympics, France and Brazil made the final. Things changed in 1988 in Seoul, when a relaxation of the rules allowed professional stars such as Brazil's Romario to play. The first semifinal in 1988 was between Italy and the Soviet Union. Italy took the lead in the second half. The Soviet Union came back and the pressure was exerted on the Italian defense, who made a poor effort at protecting the goal area, leading to a scramble at the goal, which resulted in a tie. The game went into overtime

▶ The brilliant Brazilian forward Romario in action in the 1988 Olympic final in Seoul. The Brazilian team finished in silver position on that occasion. Romario went on to play professional soccer in the Netherlands.

▲ A dazzling display of skill from one of the Argentinian players in Seoul. Argentina defeated the home team, South Korea, 2–1.

with the score at 1–1. The Soviets proved too strong in the last part of the game, and a strong shot from just outside the goal net put them ahead. Their victory was assured with a brilliant kick from the tightest possible angle that left the Italian goalkeeper sprawling, wondering how it could have gone in.

In the other semifinal the Brazilians faced the Germans. The Germans scored first, but a tying goal from Romario ensured a penalty shoot-out. The Germans were not up to it. Wolfram Wuttke saw his shot blocked and with it Germany's gold medal hopes.

In the Olympic final, the Brazilians scored first from a floating corner kick that evaded the Soviet goalkeeper. The ball fell nicely for Romario and was knocked to the back of the net by another player. The Soviets fought back, as they did in the semifinals. The Brazilian defense then fouled Mikhailichenko and conceded a penalty, which Dobrovolsky converted into a score. The game went into over-time. Brazil missed an open goal and then failed to prevent a surging run by the Soviet Savichev. He followed this with a bold chip over the goalkeeper's head, finally bringing the Olympic gold back to Eastern Europe.

▶ In 1988, the Soviet Union was the new Olympic soccer champion. Here, the Soviet players celebrate.

16

FIELD HOCKEY

Field hockey, as it is known to distinguish it from ice hockey, first appeared in the Olympic program in 1908 in London. The event was won by an English team. The only other opponents also came from the British Isles — Ireland, Scotland, and Wales. The final saw the English comfortably beating the Irish 8 – 1. After World War I the game started to spread internationally, and in Antwerp in 1920, France, Belgium, and Denmark contested the English supremacy. The 1920 English team had among it a player from the 1908 winning team, Stanley Shoveller, who no doubt brought his experience to bear in his team's unbeaten record.

There was no tournament in 1924, but the game returned to the Olympics for good in 1928 in Amsterdam. With its return came a complete shift of balance as India made its first appearance. The Indians, who learned the game from the colonizing British, took an instant liking to it and made rapid progress. Unlike in cricket, where it took much longer for India to beat

▼ The Indian team in action during the 1928 Games in Amsterdam. Striker Dhyan Chand prepares for a shot on goal.

▲ The victorious Indian hockey team pictured with their Dutch opponents.

England, their hockey prowess quickly established them on the world stage. The first Indian field hockey clubs were formed around Calcutta, and by 1926 players were competing in international matches. The two leading players of the team were goalkeeper Richard Allen and ball striker Dhyan Chand. They were the key players in three successive Olympic victories up to World War II. In the first, in 1928, they won all five games by an average margin of six goals. They themselves conceded not a single goal.

Four years later the entire Indian nation, inspired by one Olympic victory, prepared to cheer their team on to another. Unfortunately no money was available to send them on the long trip to Los Angeles. An appeal to the great leader Mohandas Gandhi was unsuccessful when he professed ignorance of the sport! However, such was the renown of the Indian team in Europe that a series of exhibition matches was organized, and the advances from these paid for their trip to the Olympics. The 1932 Olympics in Los Angeles were a triumph for the Indians. They beat Japan 11−1 and the United States 24−1. This defeat of the United States was the largest in international field hockey history.

Another four years were to pass, but as assuredly as the Olympics came around, so too did the Indians win the gold. Only the first half of the 1936 final against Germany was a close affair for the Indians, who went in at halftime only one goal up. The final score was 8−1. The Germans had used up all their energy trying to prevent the Indians from scoring in the first half.

A twelve year break because of World War II and India's independence from the British changed much in the hockey world. The break from the colonial past also meant the setting up of the state of Pakistan within India. Although not an immediate threat, Pakistan's appearance at the tournament was eagerly anticipated. This time, however, the Indians had a chance to beat their former rulers on the hockey field. It was the first time that an opportunity for such a contest had occurred. Both teams had advanced easily to the final, giving up only two goals and scoring forty-two between them. The final was a one-sided affair, and to the Indians their victory over the British was a very special one.

In that tournament Pakistan signaled its emerging ability. However, the Indians continued to win and by the time of the 1960 Games in Rome, their winning streak had extended to thirty consecutive Olympic victories. Only the Pakistani team seemed capable of upsetting them. Silver medalists in Melbourne in 1956, when they lost by 1−0 in the final, Pakistan seemed the team most likely to cause an upset. The first hint of such an upset came in the early rounds when Australia forced the Indians into fifteen minutes of overtime before finally giving in. Things hardly looked much brighter for India in the semifinals, when they managed to beat the British team by a single goal. India's opposition in the final, Pakistan, were perhaps hungrier for victory, and after twelve minutes they scored. This single score brought them the Olympic title and brought an end to the most remarkable succession of victories in Olympic history.

Four years later in Tokyo, the Indian team was back in winning form. But since the defeat of the Indians, other teams no longer saw them as invincible. Undiscouraged and with everything to gain, teams from all over the world lined up to try their chance against them. In Mexico in 1968, Pakistan, New Zealand, and Australia all had strong teams. The latter two teams both beat the Indians 2−1. The conceding of two goals was unprecedented, but as so often happens, once the impossible has occurred it becomes commonplace. India has never again climbed to its former heights.

The first women's Olympic field hockey tournament was held in Moscow in 1980. The winners were a team from Zimbabwe. It signaled a change in the women's game. According to Alison Ramsay, the British team's midfield player in 1988: ''The game is so fast now that we play all our games on artificial turf. The traditional type of hockey player — you know, enormous, burly — just doesn't exist any more. We are athletes. You need a slim, light build to play hockey these days.'' Ramsay was referring to a modern game that requires speed combined with accurate passing and shooting. The hockey ball has been timed at 60 mph (97 kph), so you need to be fast to handle a pass or a block.

▶ Germany against the Netherlands in 1984.

▼ Germany (in the red and blue) tied 2 – 2 with Australia in the women's field hockey competition in Los Angeles in 1984.

The women's tournament in Seoul in 1988 proved to be extremely exciting. The British team progressed to the semifinals thanks to a tie with the United States in the round robin stage. (The teams play each other, and the teams with the highest number of points go through to the next stage.) In front of a crowd of 25,000, the British played the home team, South Korea, in their semifinal. A goal after eighteen minutes sealed the British fate and put the host nation in the final.

In the other half of the competition, the Australians produced the shock of the tournament by beating the team from the Netherlands in the semifinal.

▼ British hockey hero of 1988, Sean Kerly.

This signaled the end of the Dutch domination of women's hockey.

The fight for the gold medal was between Australia and South Korea. Despite the tremendous support for the home team, the Australians, captained by the brilliant Debbie Bowman, won.

Alongside teams from Australia and New Zealand, the Europeans have started to gain a place in the men's field hockey world. Going into the finals in Seoul in 1988, the favorites were Britain, West Germany, Australia, and the Netherlands. As it turned out, the British, who placed third in Los Angeles in 1984, did themselves justice, with strength and a little luck. The West Germans, with their star center-forward Stefan Blocher, raced through the early rounds. But in the semifinals against the Netherlands, Blocher was knocked unconscious by a blow from a stray stick and was unable to continue playing in the tournament. It was a defensive German team that took the field, but they could not contain Britain's Imran Sherwani, who made two goals, and Sean Kerly, who scored one. The British team took hockey's highest prize. It was a great day for the victors, who had been part-time players until their success in Los Angeles gave them a belief in their world-class abilities.

► Victory is ours! The moment of joy for the British men's field hockey team in Seoul.

HANDBALL

The sport of handball is a thrilling and exciting indoor game that can best be described as a mixture of soccer and basketball. The ball is passed in quick-fire succession up the field until, near the goal, the player throws it at the back of the net. The current game evolved from several different versions played around the world, especially in Eastern Europe. In Germany an outdoor version with eleven players on each team gained some popularity at the same time as a seven-a-side game was being developed in the Soviet Union. It was the Dutch version that had the first success on the international stage, with a demonstration given in Amsterdam during the Olympic Games of 1928. By 1936, the Amateur Handball Federation had twenty-three affiliated countries. At the Berlin Games in that year the German team beat all their opposition. Only the Austrians made a fight of it in the final. This, however, was the end of the outdoor game, for after World War II the seven-player indoor version made a strong return for a number of reasons.

▲ Emotional tears of joy from the South Korean women after their surprise victory in the 1988 Olympic handball final.

Orignally, there was the popularity of soccer as the main outdoor winter sport in Europe. Then the return of the indoor game was influenced by East European coaches, who introduced the sport to many other countries. Finally, the indoor game encouraged the development of a fast, athletic, and dynamic sport, full of spectacular athletic feats by the players. The final stages of an attack involve precision shooting and fearless goalkeeping. Both are integral parts of the game. The continuing success of the East European and Scandinavian teams is a result of their very cold winters, which encourage indoor sports. The game has yet to really catch on in

▶ A Soviet player is held back by two Koreans in the women's handball competition in Seoul in 1988.

Western Europe. In some parts of the United States interest in the game almost equals that of basketball.

The new game reentered Olympic competition in the 1972 Munich Games. The reigning men's world champions, Romania, came to the Olympics with a good deal of confidence. However, it was the Czechoslovakians who faced Yugoslavia in the final. The Yugoslavians easily won and became the first Olympic men's handball champions for nearly forty years. At the following Olympics, in Montreal in 1976, the women's game was included. The Soviets dominated both the men's and women's events. Again the Romanian

men had come as world champions and again they were disappointed with their second place finish. The East European domination persisted throughout the 1980s, but the greatest upset came in Seoul in 1988. The highly regarded South Koreans, the Games' hosts, combatted the superior strength of the Soviets with their own special skills. In the Suwon gymnasium, 25 miles outside Seoul, the Korean

▶ A Soviet player launches the ball in the men's handball final in Seoul.

men's team, however, failed to overcome the might of the Soviets who produced a superior display of tactics and speed. The Norwegians took the bronze and signaled the revival of Scandinavian interest in the sport. The Soviets also took the bronze in the women's event, having won the titles in 1976 and 1980.

The women's handball competition in Seoul was won by the South

▲ The men's handball final in Seoul was hotly contested by the Soviet Union and the host nation, South Korea (in red).

Koreans. In a tensely fought battle against the Soviet Union — who had won the first women's competition in 1976, and four years later in Moscow — they eventually squeezed a win 21–19. The competition in 1984 in Los Angeles was won by Yugoslavia.

BASKETBALL

Basketball was invented by Dr. James Naismith in Massachusetts at the end of the nineteenth century. Not surprisingly, American teams have dominated the sport internationally for a long time. Basketball was introduced at Olympic level in 1936, and the United States was unbeaten until 1972. The first finals in Berlin in 1936 were played outdoors on courts of clay and sand. An attempt to ban players taller than 6 feet was overturned, and American Joe Fortenberry, at just over 6½ feet tall, became the first Olympic basketball star. In the final, rain had so affected the court that the American game against Canada had to be played in a sea of mud. Dribbling the ball was difficult, and Fortenberry's score of eight points was remarkable. The match ended 19 − 8. Fortenberry had scored as many points as the entire Canadian team.

In 1948 in London, the American domination held. Height was no longer an issue, as one Chinese player

▼ Switzerland battles in vain to stop the United States from scoring at the 1948 Games in London. The Americans won the gold medal.

The U.S. basketball captain in 1948, J. B. Renick (number 55) watches as teammate A. J. Groza (number 15) scores two points.

demonstrated by going through the legs of Bob Kurland, who stood 6 feet 7 inches tall, and following through to score. This did not turn out to be very significant; the United States won the final, and the Chinese came in eighteenth overall. On the way to the final, the Americans came up against strong opposition for the first time when Argentina pushed them close to defeat, with the final score of 59 – 57.

The consistency of the American team was a problem for other countries over the years. The exasperation caused by the domination of one country in a team sport leads their opponents to think of extreme ways to disrupt their game. Tactics are devised to nullify the skills of the opponent. In the case of basketball, a tactic known as the ''freeze out'' was used by the Soviet team in Helsinki in 1952. Following a heavy defeat by the United States in the round robin, they decided not to imitate the Americans' game and instead tried to maintain possession of the ball at all costs, which meant avoiding offensive play, or trying to score points. At halftime

the score was only 17–15 in favor of the United States. These tactics seemed to be working. But when the United States gained a lead they themselve froze the game. The Soviets got a taste of their own medicine, and one team member even sat down!

▲ American Bob Kurland attempts to score in the controversial game between the United States and the Soviet Union in Helsinki in 1952.

The Uruguayans wanted desperately to be on the medalist's podium in 1952. This aim was to have been achieved without much reference to the Olympic motto, especially the part that says: ''the essential thing is not to have conquered but to have fought well.'' For this team the essential thing was fighting! In their match against France they fouled so much that they were down to only three players. At the end of the game they argued with the referee, who they thought had disallowed them a basket that would have tied the score. By the time he had made it clear that the points stood, the Uruguayan team was in such disarray that the French were able to use the last seconds of the game to score. The Uruguayans were now so furious they kicked the American referee, Vincent Farrell, and he had to be carried from the stadium. The Uruguayans next played the Soviet Union, causing three injuries in the second half. They then needed to beat Argentina to win the bronze medal. ''Beat'' is an unfortunate word in these circumstances since the match degenerated at one point into a brawl. But the Uruguayans won, came in third overall, and presumably returned to their country as heroes.

In following years, American domination was little affected by the tricks of other lesser teams. Their winning margins in 1956 were all over 30 points; in 1960 the average margin of victory was 40 points. The 1960 American team had ten members who went on to play at the professional level. The Soviets were relegated to an almost fixed second place. In 1964

they actually took the lead, but the Americans came back to win. The growing strength of the Yugoslavians was apparent in 1968, when they managed to hold the United States to a 15-point victory. They eventually won the silver medal, pushing the Soviets out of the second place they had won in the previous four Olympic Games.

In 1972 in Munich, the great winning streak of the United States came to an end in one of the most famous of sporting controversies. After 62 straight wins the United States met their defeat. Depending on your view, they lost at the hands of either Soviet star Sasha Belov, who scored the final contested basket; or R. William Jones, the Secretary of the International Basketball Association, who added extra time to the game; or a biased inquiry board.

The story is simply that the American team, winning by 50−49 and with one second to play, found that the last of its two penalty shots had been disallowed. Then, three seconds were added to the clock, in which time Belov scored. Thus the Soviet team won by 51−50. The panel of inquiry threw out the protest, and the American players voted unanimously to refuse their silver medals. There are several different sides in this controversy

▶ The American players rally around as a team member attempts to score against Italy in the Rome Games in 1960. The United States went on to win the gold medal.

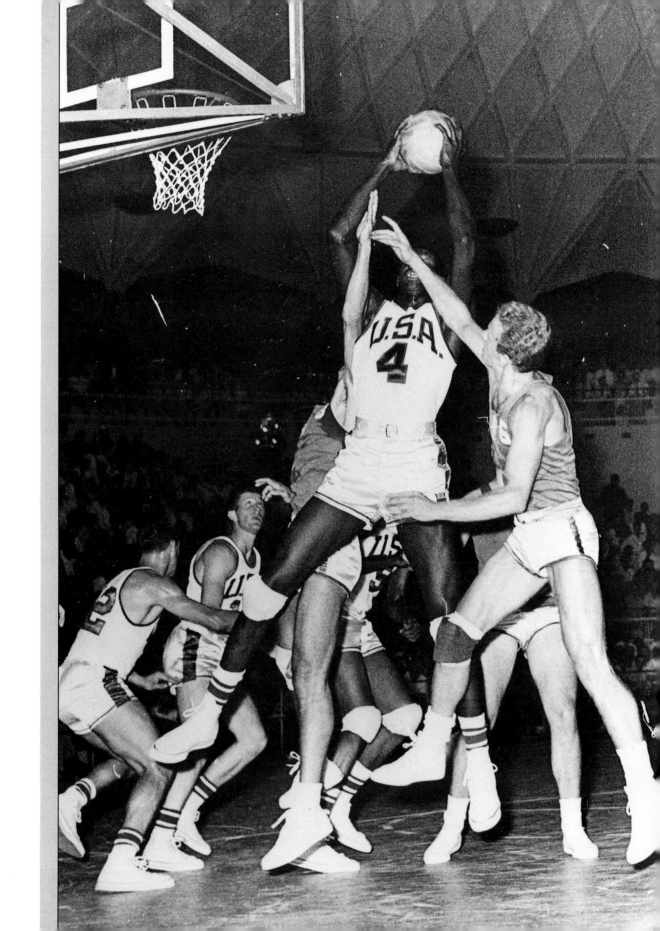

but the refusal of the head referee, Renato Righetto, to sign the score sheet at the end is significant. He thought the addition of the three seconds was "irregular" and against the rules.

Four years later the United States was back on top of the roster, though not without difficulty. One of the potential members of the American team, Butch Lee, was excluded at the last minute from the Olympic squad. His response was to play on the Puerto Rican team. In its match against the United States, the Puerto Rican team was beaten by only one basket. Unfortunately the much anticipated

◀ The men's Olympic basketball title in Seoul was contested by Yugoslavia and the Soviet Union. The Soviets were the victors.

▼ The victorious Soviet men's team in 1988.

▲ The Soviet coach Alexander Gomelsky is tossed in the air by his jubiliant players after their victory in Seoul.

rematch between the United States and the Soviet Union did not occur, since the Yugoslavians beat the Soviets in the semifinals and won the silver.

Because of the boycotts of 1980 and 1984 the United States and the Soviet Union did not compete. In 1988 the Yugoslavians upset the applecart by beating the Americans in an earlier round. Rimas Kourtinaitis was the top scorer with 28 baskets in a final score of 82 – 76. The final was between the Soviets and the Yugoslavians. The latter felt that they had a good chance, since earlier in the year they had beaten the Soviets four times, as well as in the opening round in Seoul. Unfortunately for the Yugoslavians it was not to be. The Soviets repeated their Munich victory to win their second Olympic basketball gold medal. The top Soviet scorer was Raimendas Martchioulenis, with 21 baskets. However, the final praise was reserved for the Soviet coach Alexander Gomelsky, a sixty-year-old veteran of six Olympic Games. He was tossed high in the air by his team at the end of the match.

The United States also dominated women's basketball for years. Despite this, a great deal of competitive spirit remained in the game. In Seoul in 1988, the U.S. team played the Soviets for the first time since 1976. This was due to the 1980 and 1984 boycotts. Fantastic performances from Cynthia Cooper and Katrina McClair, who spearheaded the American attacks and were quick on defense, led to a 102 – 88 victory for the United States. The team went on to beat the Yugoslavians in the final, 77 – 70.

◀ True Olympic spirit is displayed here as Andre Lloyd of the United States is helped to her feet by two Soviet opponents in Seoul.

▼ Players and coaches from the U.S. women's basketball team look on anxiously as their team competes in the final in Seoul.

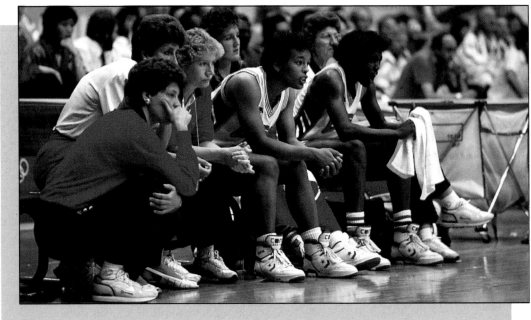

VOLLEYBALL

This sport was first developed in 1895 by a physical education instructor, William Morgan, in Massachusetts. He gave it the name "Minotonette." The game really took off as volleyball worldwide because it could be played so easily. All that was needed was a ball and a net. With no need for expensive equipment, it became popular all over the world, especially in countries where finance for sports facilities was limited. This fast team game is played in 157 affiliated countries, by more than 70 million registered players. It is also a popular beach sport, since sand is an excellent surface to learn on.

Volleyball teams have five members. The object is to ground the ball on the other side of the net. The match is played to the best of five sets, as in men's tennis, with a set lasting 15 points. You score only when you have the serve, which you win if you take a point against the opposing team's serve. The game was introduced to the

▼ An early women's volleyball match between India and Bulgaria.

Olympics in Tokyo in 1964. The host nation then had a history of success in volleyball, hence their enthusiasm to have it played in the Olympics. However, there were at this time many other strong teams, particularly the Soviet Union, Czechoslovakia, and Romania.

In the women's event at Tokyo the Japanese were overwhelmingly favored. Their attempts were nearly ruined at the opening, when a last-minute withdrawal by the North Koreans left the competition one team short. But the Japanese were not going to be stopped. They persuaded the South Koreans to send a team instead. The reason for their eagerness to compete was a team made up mostly of women from a spinning mill near Osaka. This team had been coached by the fierce trainer Daimatsu. He made them train six hours a day, seven days a week, for virtually the whole year. Their supremacy was awesome. For many Japanese people they came to symbolize their country's hard work to overcome the adversity of the years after World War II. They lost only one set in the tournament. The whole of Japan was enraptured by their

▼ The Israeli and Indian men's volleyball teams battle for victory in a ''friendly'' game in 1952. India won the game by three sets to none.

achievement, and when it came to the final, almost everyone in the country watched the game on television. It has been estimated that in the history of sports no event has ever been watched

▲ Munich in 1972 bore witness to the emergence of the Japanese as the dominant men's volleyball team following the Japanese victory over East Germany in the final. Here, the delighted players are celebrating their win.

by such a large proportion of a country's population as on that night, when over 80 percent of Japan was watching.

In the event the women's team won in straight sets, with not much excitement or drama to the game. But a true sports fan will say that a score like that is *really* exciting. The Japanese men's team did not fare as well as predicted against very strong opposition. They did, however, beat

▲ The women's volleyball final in Munich in 1972 was a fierce duel between the Soviet Union and the improving Japanese team. The game went to a nail-biting fifth set when the Soviets clinched victory.

the eventual winners, the Soviet Union, in an earlier round. However, they could not beat the Czechoslovakians, who ended with an equal number of victories to those of the Soviets, but with a lower point total.

Four years later the Japanese men's team went one better, coming in second to the Soviets. The women, however, had to cede their domination to the Soviets, losing to them in four sets, taking the silver medal. In Munich in 1972, the Japanese men finally made it to the highest step on the podium, beating the emerging new talent of Germany. The women, for the second time running, found the Soviets just too strong. For the first time the final went to five sets, with the Japanese women coming back in the second and fourth sets, only to lose the fifth 11−15. The domination by the Japanese has since been under threat not only from their old adversaries, the Soviets, but also from the newly emerging talents of the United States in the men's game and China and Peru in the women's.

The growth of the American men's team can be dated from 1981. Before then they were not a serious threat. In 1984 they shocked the volleyball world with a victory in the final of the Los Angeles Games. The lack of Soviet involvement due to the boycott somewhat devalued the victory, so coming to Seoul in 1988, the American team had a lot to prove. This team was made up of several veterans, including the star player Karch Kiraly. All in their late twenties, they had younger and more fit opposition to contend with. The Soviets, on the other hand, were entering without their big hitter Savin and with doubts about thirty-six-year-old Viatcheslav Zaitsev, a veteran of the 1976 and 1980 Olympic teams. The Japanese no longer proved to be a threat, since their speed could not compensate for their lack of height, an increasingly important factor. The Americans beat them in straight sets, their twenty-eighth straight win over the Japanese. The domination of the American team in the early rounds marked them as stiff competition for the Soviets. However, they were yet to face a different sort of problem. They were forced to play first thing in the morning so that the audience in the United States could watch them in the early evening. When it came to the final, however, the game was held at a more usual time, leaving the exciting prospect of watching the two superpowers battling on a volleyball court for the first time in twenty years — with the United States as previous winners. Many Americans stayed up half the night to watch!

For the first three-quarters of an hour of the final, the Soviets looked as though they might overturn the American team. The first set went to the Soviets, but the Americans began to wake up toward the end, forcing eight set points. This caused a turn around. The Soviets fell into disarray and even the introduction of the great Zaitsev could not turn the tide. The United States won a famous victory in four sets. This signaled the end of an era with the retirement of their coach, Marv Dunphy, and top players, Kiraly,

Timmons, and Craig Buck. It is likely, though, that the American team's inspirational play will spark sufficient interest among young people to ensure a continuing flow of talent to join the United States team.

The women's volleyball game is now widely considered even better viewing than the men's. Longer rallies lead to more exciting points being contested, and the number of countries with excellent teams is large enough for upsets to occur more regularly. The attractiveness of the women's competition compared with the men's is reflected in the average length of the matches. The men's last on average 3.67 sets, while the women's last on average 4.15 sets.

▲ The star of the U.S. men's volleyball team in Seoul, Karch Kiraly, is photographed here in the shadow of the American flag.

This is a far cry from 1964 when the Japanese women were so dominant and competition was so scarce that they called in an extra team to make up numbers. The only absentee team from Seoul in 1988 was the favored Cuban team. But the standard was so high they were not particularly missed after the competition started.

The first game in Seoul brought together Japan and the Soviet Union.

► Can the Soviet player stop the powerful Kiraly spike? He prepares to prevent him in the 1988 Olympic final.

This was a thrilling game that lasted five sets. The Soviets had four match points but the Japanese held on and took the first match point. Mokoto Obayashi was the heroine, first playing an excellent block and then the winning "spike." This is the shot by the player at the net who attempts to ground the ball with a strong downward smash.

The stars of the 1988 Games were undoubtedly the Peruvians. After beating the Brazilians in straight sets, they were involved in four consecutive five-set thrillers. In a replay of the 1984 women's Olympic final, the American team could not beat the Chinese this time. Peru first showed its real mettle against the Chinese team.

▼ Some of the Peruvian volleyball players celebrate with tears of emotion following their dramatic semifinal victory over the Japanese in Seoul.

▲ The United States team was pitted against China in an early round in Seoul in 1988. It was a replay of the 1984 Olympic final. The Chinese team emerged as victors.

In five exciting sets Peru triumphed, coming back from 2−1 down. Against the United States they came back from 2−0 down to win in five sets, their star being Gabriela Perez. She was only twenty years old but had a coolness of purpose that inspired her team to return from the brink of defeat. In the semifinals the Peruvians for once did not seem to be running their game so close to disaster as they grabbed the first two sets. But the Japanese battled back in the next two sets to make it 2−2. Eventually, after much excitement, Peru made its way to the final by winning the last set 15−13.

For the final, a fanatical crowd arrived in the Hanyang University gym, firmly behind this Peruvian team that seemed permanently in the habit of tempting the jaws of defeat only to seize victory in the end. Their support was at its most vocal as the Peruvians won the first two sets. Suddenly the Soviets moved up a gear to pull back the next two sets and lead 5−0 in the last. The Peruvians came back to lead 11−10 then, saving a match point at 15−14, they had three match points themselves. But the Soviet block was impassable now, and at match point against them, the Peruvians could not stop the Soviet Union who won 17−15. It was one of the great team matches in Olympic history.

▲ The 1988 women's Olympic volleyball final between Peru and the Soviet Union was one of the greatest games ever played.

▶ The star of ther 1988 Seoul Games for the Peruvians was their statuesque volleyball player, Gabriela Perez.

GLOSSARY

Adversaries Opponents.

Affiliated Connected with or joined to a group or organization.

Amateur Someone who takes part in something for the love of it, or to win, but not for money.

Boycott To refuse to have dealings with a person or organization as a protest.

Collaboration When more than one person or country work together.

Colonist Someone who settles in another country.

Contention Something that causes a dispute or disagreement.

Croquet A game in which wooden balls have to be hit by mallets through a series of small hoops.

Intimidation The use of threats (usually of violence) to influence another person's actions.

Invincible Not able to be defeated or overcome.

Nationalistic Strongly devoted to the interests of one's country or nation.

Partisan Devotedly following a person, cause, or team.

Professional Someone who plays sports for financial gain.

Prolific Producing constantly successful results.

Roque A game developed from croquet. It is played on a hard surface with a strong border from which the ball can be rebounded.

Successor Someone who follows in another's place.

FURTHER READING

Frommer, Harvey. *Olympic Controversies.* New York: Franklin Watts, 1987.

Glubock, Shirley, and Alfred Tamarin. *Olympic Games in Ancient Greece.* New York: Harper Junior Books, 1976.

Greenberg, Stan, ed. *The Guinness Book of Olympic Facts and Feats.* New York: Bantam, 1984.

Marshall, Nancy Thies. *Women Who Compete.* Old Tappan, N.J.: Fleming H. Revell Company, 1988.

Tatlow, Peter. *The Olympics.* New York: Franklin Watts, 1988.

Walczewski, Michael. *The Olympic Fun Fact Book.* New York: Dell, 1988.

Wallechinsky, David. *The Complete Book of the Olympics.* New York: Penguin Books, 1988.

INDEX